My first

I can draw . . .

Cute
and Cuddly

Follow the simple steps
to learn how to draw lots
of charming characters.

·

Tear out the practice pages
to perfect your pictures before
drawing them in the scenes.

Cuddly kittens

1 Draw an oval head and add a body.

2 Add two triangles for the ears.

Try drawing your own . . .

3 Draw four straight lines for the legs.

4 Draw a wiggly line for the tail.

5 Give the kitten a face. You could add stripes!

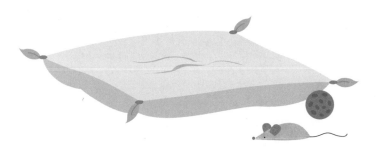

Guinea pigs

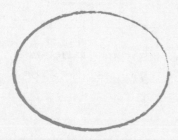

1

Draw an oval
for the body.

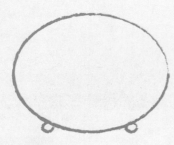

2

Add two little feet.

3

Give the guinea
pig an eye, an ear,
and a little nose.

4

Add long whiskers.

Bouncing bunnies

1

Draw a circle for the head and add a body.

2

Add two big ears and two front paws.

3

Draw a circle for the tail.

4

Give the bunny a happy face.

Huggable **hamsters**

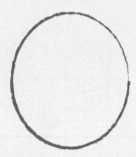

1

Draw an oval for the body.

2

Add two semicircles for the ears.

3

Give the hamster a sweet face.

4

Draw two front paws and two back paws.

Try drawing your own . . .

Paddling **ducklings**

1

Draw a circle for
the head and a
slightly larger circle
for the body.

2

Add two wings.

3

Draw two triangles
and two lines
for the feet.

4

Draw a triangle for
the beak and add
two eyes - quack!

Micro pigs

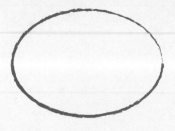

1 Draw an oval for the body.

2 Add two ears.

Try drawing your own . . .

3 Draw four lines for the legs.

4 Add a circle for the snout and a curly line for the tail.

5 Give the micro pig two big eyes - oink!

Perfect puppies

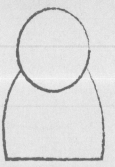

1 Draw an oval for the head and add the body.

2 Add two floppy ears.

Try drawing your own . . .

3 Draw two front paws.

4 Add two ovals for the back feet.

5 Give the puppy a face with a wet nose.

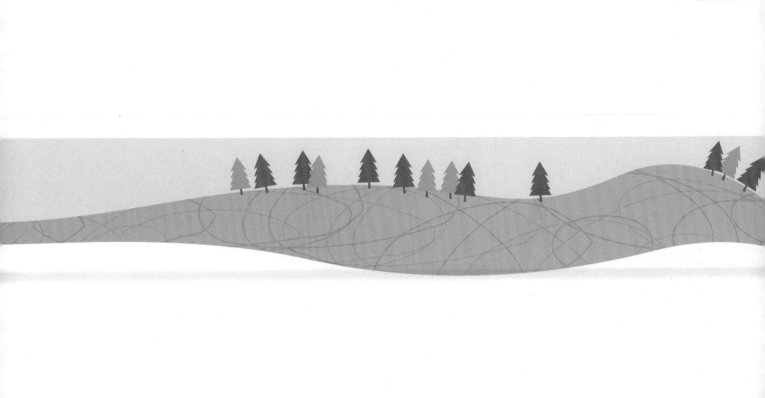

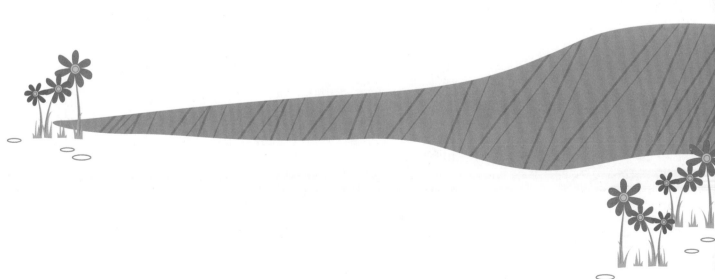

Prickly **hedgehogs**

1

Draw
the body.

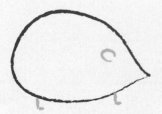

2

Add the legs
and an ear.

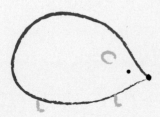

3

Give the hedgehog
an eye and a nose.

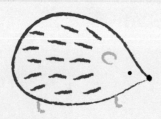

4

Draw lots of little
lines for the
hedgehog's prickles.

Tabby cats

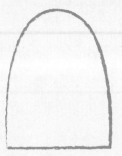

1 Draw a long semicircle for the body.

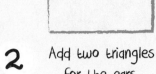

2 Add two triangles for the ears.

Try drawing your own . . .

3 Draw a curly line for the tail.

4 Give the cat a cute face.

5 Add lots of stripes to finish the tabby.

Playful pugs

1
Draw the head and body.

2
Add two ears and a tail.

3
Draw four little legs.

4
Give the pug a face with a cute nose!

Try drawing your own . . .

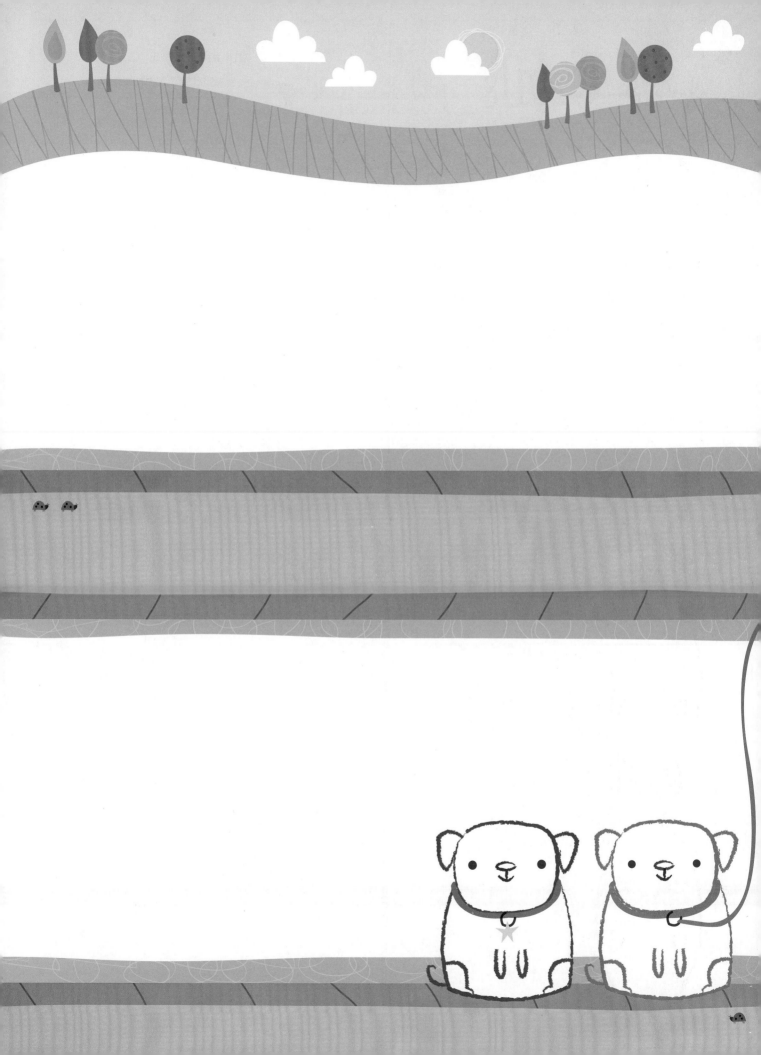

Gentle gerbils

1

Draw an oval for the body.

2

Add four little legs.

3

Draw two semicircles for the ears and add a wiggly line for the tail.

4

Give the gerbil a happy face and don't forget the whiskers!

Try drawing your own . . .

Bumbling bears

1 Draw a circle for the head and add two long arms.

2 Add two semicircles for the ears and draw the tummy.

Try drawing your own . . .

3 Draw two ovals for the feet.

4 Add a cute face.

5 Give the bear two rosy cheeks!

Lovely **Labradors**

1

Draw a head and add a circle for the nose.

2

Add the body and two ears.

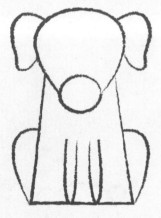

3

Draw two front paws and two back legs.

4

Give the Labrador a cute face and a wiggly line for the tail.

Shetland ponies

1 Draw an oval for the body and add a head.

2 Add four lines for the legs.

Try drawing your own . . .

3 Draw two tiny ears and a line for the nose.

4 Add lots of lines for the mane and tail.

5 Give the shetland pony two eyes and nostrils.

Sleepy kittens

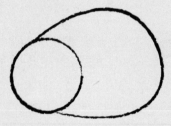

1

Draw a circle for the head and add the body.

2

Add a line for the long tail.

3

Draw two triangles for the ears.

4

Give the sleeping kitten a sweet face.

Try drawing your own . . . .

Munching macaws

1

Draw the head and add an oval body.

2

Draw a big beak

3

Draw a wing and a triangle for the tail.

4

Give the macaw an eye and two legs.

Try drawing your own . . . .

Posing poodles

1 Draw an oval for the head and a triangle for the nose.

2 Add two ears and give the poodle two eyes and a big nose.

Try drawing your own . . .

3 Draw the body.

4 Add lines for the legs and tail.

5 Add circles for the feet and the pompom on the tail.

Prancing
ponies

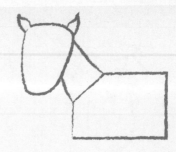

1 Draw the head and neck.

2 Add two ears and part of a rectangle for the body.

Try drawing your own . . .

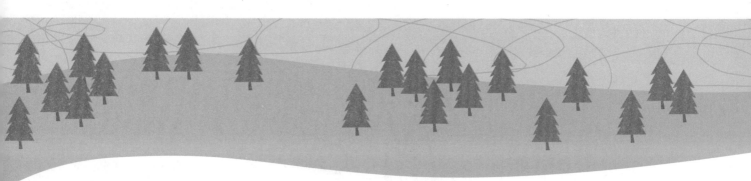

3 Draw four lines for the legs.

4 Add a shaggy mane and a curved line for the tail.

5 Draw two eyes and nostrils and add a line for the nose.

Shaggy sheepdogs

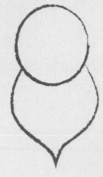

1

Draw a circle for the head and add a furry chest.

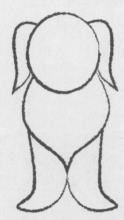

2

Add two ears and two front legs.

3

Draw two back legs.

4

Give the sheepdog a shaggy face and a little tongue.

Try drawing your own . . . .

Bright budgies

1 Draw an oval for the head and add the body.

2 Add two feathery wings.

Try drawing your own . . .

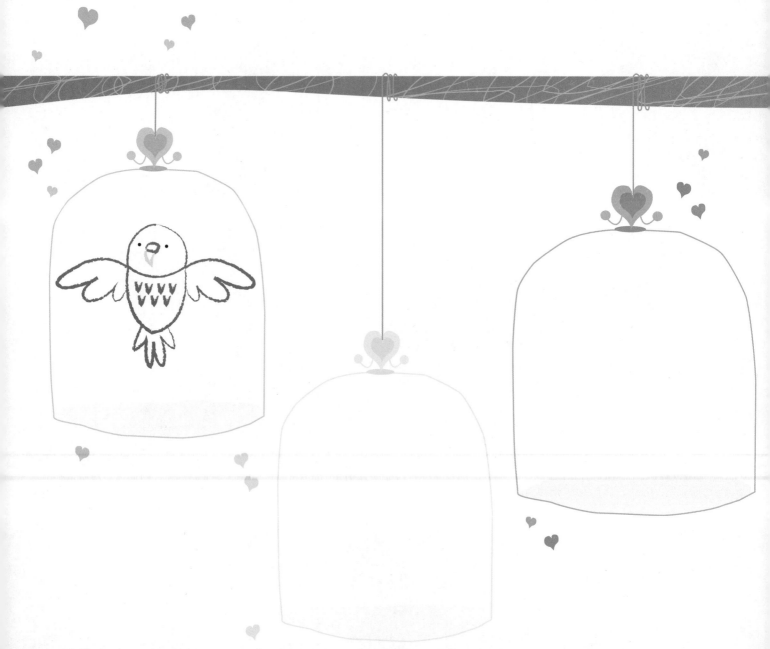

3 Draw a tail of big feathers.

4 Draw some triangles for the feathers on the chest.

5 Give the budgie two eyes and a sharp beak.

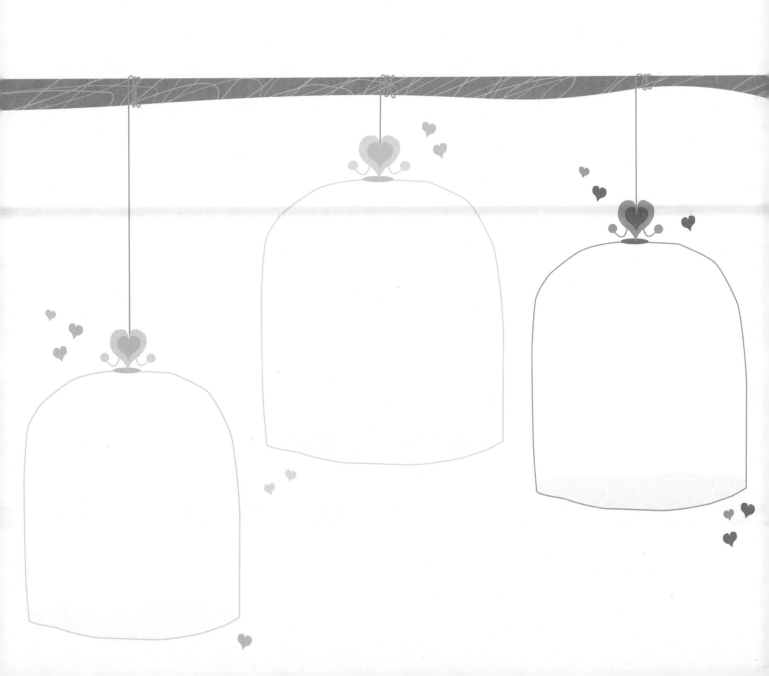